D1324471

Songs *from* Around a Toadstool Table

Follett
Publishing
Company

CHICAGO

NEW YORK

Rowena Bennett

Songs *from* Around a Toadstool Table

Illustrated by Betty Fraser

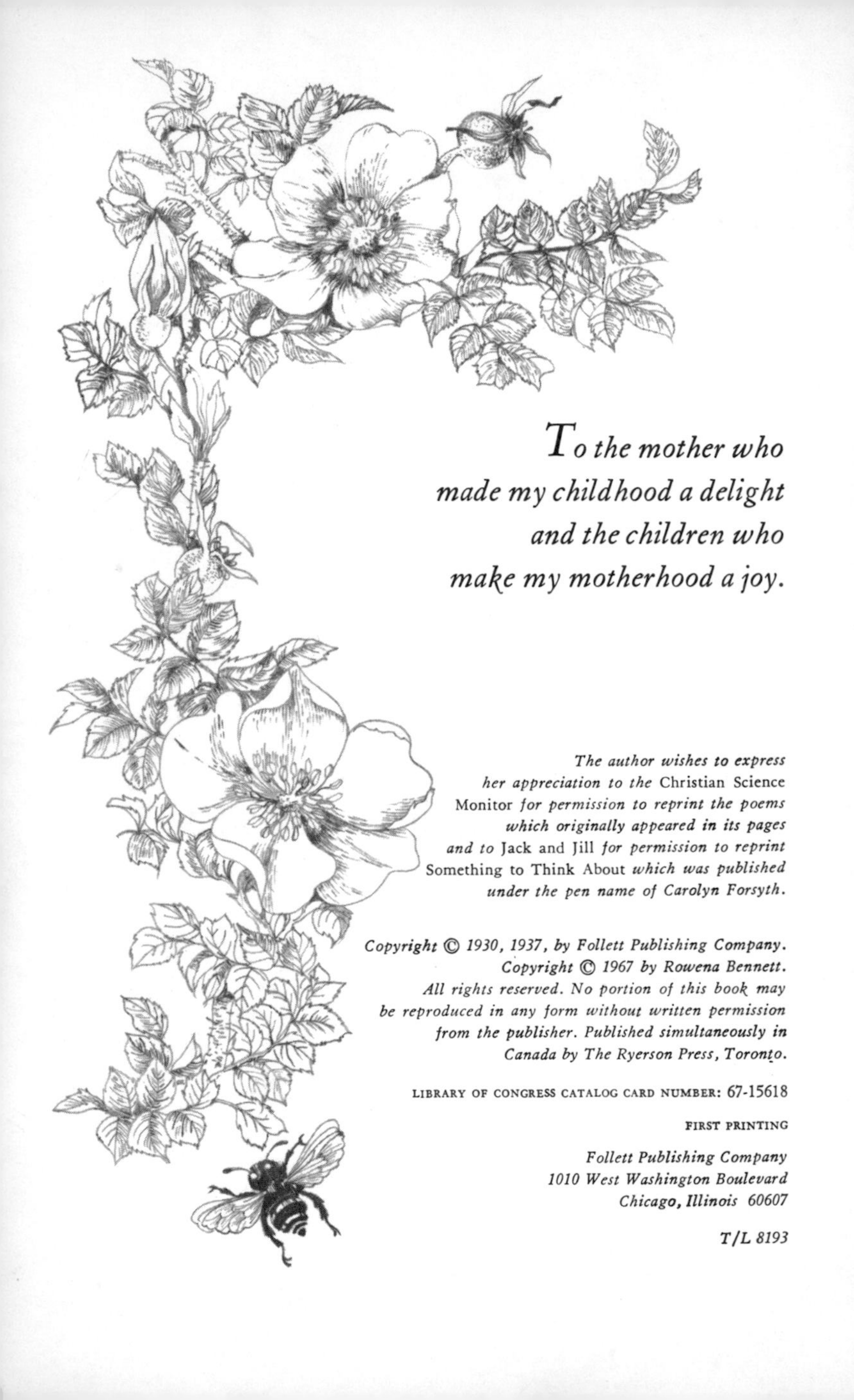

To the mother who
made my childhood a delight
and the children who
make my motherhood a joy.

The author wishes to express her appreciation to the Christian Science Monitor *for permission to reprint the poems which originally appeared in its pages and to* Jack and Jill *for permission to reprint* Something to Think About *which was published under the pen name of Carolyn Forsyth.*

 Published simultaneously in Canada by The Ryerson Press, Toronto.

LIBRARY OF CONGRESS CATALOG CARD NUMBER: 67-15618

FIRST PRINTING

Follett Publishing Company
1010 West Washington Boulevard
Chicago, Illinois 60607

T/L 8193

A List of the Poems

Songs
from
Around a Toadstool Table

Around a Toadstool Table

Around a toadstool table
I dine with fairy kings;
Across the moon-white hilltops
I dance in fairy rings;
And when I sleep, I nestle
Where fairies fold their wings.

Under the Tent of the Sky

The wind cracked his whip,
The storm flashed a gun,
And the animal-clouds marched one by one
Under the tent of the sky.

There were elephants, blue,
And shaggy white bears,
And dozens and dozens of prancing gray mares
With their beautiful heads held high.

There were soft-footed panthers
And ostriches, fluffy,
And a great hippopotamus, purple and puffy,
Who wallowed in mud-colored mist.

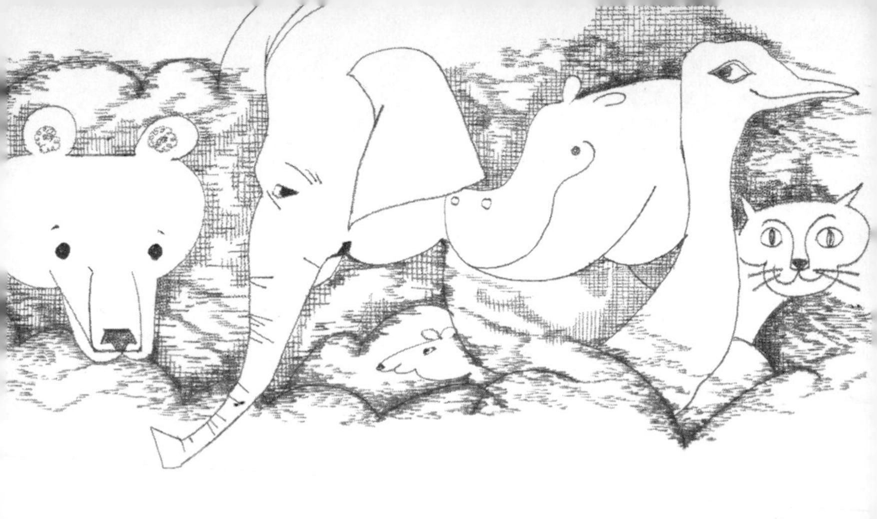

There were small curly dogs
And camels with humps
And a wrinkled rhinoceros, all over bumps,
With a horn as big as your fist.

There was even a lion
Bedecked with a mane
Who growled so loud that he turned into rain
And tumbled to earth with a sigh.

The wind cracked his whip
And out came the sun
And the animal-clouds passed one by one
Out of the tent of the sky.

Spring Carnival

The wind blew his bugle,
the rain beat his drum.
The sun, like a herald
cried joyfully, "Come!
Come to the carnival, Spring."

So the tulips all came
in their dresses of flame,
And a snowdrop was there
with a star in her hair
To dance at the carnival, Spring.

Pussy Willows

I came on them yesterday (merely by chance),
Those newly born pussies, asleep on a branch;
Each curled up so tight in a fluff of a ball
That I could not see ear-points or tail-tips at all;
But I thought that I heard, when the March
wind was stirring,
A soft little sound like the low note of purring.
I wonder if they would have leaped from their
bough
And arched their wee backs with a frightened
"Meow!"
If I had dared tell them in one warning cry
That a fierce patch of dogwood was growing
close by.

Meeting the Easter Bunny

On Easter morn at early dawn
before the cocks were crowing,
I met a bobtail bunnykin
and asked where he was going,
" 'Tis in the house and out the house
a-tipsy, tipsy-toeing,
'Tis round the house and 'bout the house
a-lightly I am going."
"But what is that of every hue
you carry in your basket?"
" 'Tis eggs of gold and eggs of blue;

I wonder that you ask it.
'Tis chocolate eggs and bonbon eggs
and eggs of red and gray,
For every child in every house
on bonny Easter Day."
He perked his ears and winked his eye
and twitched his little nose;
He shook his tail—what tail he had—
and stood up on his toes.
"I must be gone before the sun;
the east is growing gray;
'Tis almost time for bells to chime."
So he hippety-hopped away.

Maying Song

Come Maying,
Come playing,
Dear lassies, blithe and fair!
The bud has burst, the leaf is green,
There is no time to spare!
Sweet May has walked across the hills
And scattered them with daffodils.

Come singing,
Come bringing
Your basket bright and gay,
And we shall hold a carnival
To greet the lovely May.

Bring garlands, spring garlands,
To strew the waiting street;
And let none pipe who can't impart
The magic to our feet;
And let none sing who cannot sing
Sweetly as Pierrot,
For May's as young and soft of tongue
As in the long ago.

So out and in, and out and in
We'll dance as light as Harlequin;
And in her robes of Lincoln green,
Sweet May herself will be our queen.

The Rain

The rain, they say, is a mouse-gray horse
That is shod with a silver shoe;
The sound of his hoofs can be heard on the roofs
As he gallops the whole night through.

Rubber Boots

Little boots and big boots,
    Traveling together
On the shiny sidewalks,
    In the rainy weather,
Little boots and big boots,
    Oh, it must be fun
To splash the silver raindrops
    About you as you run,
Or scatter bits of rainbow
    Beneath the April sun!
Big boots and little boots,

You know how it feels
To have the white clouds drifting
Far below your heels;
And it is dizzy pleasure,
Along the way to school,
To walk the lacy tree tops
That lie in every pool.

Little boots and big boots,
How you like to putter
In every slender streamlet
That scampers down the gutter!

How you like to dabble
  Where the current crinkles
And fill the flowing water
  With new and wider wrinkles;

Or stir the yellow clay up
  To sudden, cloudy puffs
That dull the shining surface
  With muddy browns or buffs.

Big boots and little boots,
  Travel on together,
Merrily go splashing
  Through April's rainy weather!

Dandelion Bubbles

Dandelion bubbles,
  Soft and white as down,
    The fairies must have blown you
      From out your pipes of brown.
They used the clouds for soap suds,
  Then, tired of their play,
    They left you on your pipe stems
      For the wind to blow away.
A young breeze passed and saw you,
  And, feeling in a huff,
    He burst you, pretty bubbles,
      With but a single puff;
But fairy breath is magic,
  And I've heard a whisper say
    Your million scattered fragments
      Will turn to gold some day.

Adventure

A runaway road passes grandfather's gate
And scampers away to the lea.
I say to it, "Please, little road, won't you wait?"
But it only cries, "Come, follow me!"
The gate whispers, "Stay!"
And the swing cries out, "Play!"
But the runaway road just scampers away,
And I'm so bewitched that I burst into laughter
And leap the low fence to go merrily after.
I've followed before, so of course
    the road knows me,
And there is no end to the secrets it shows me:
A meadowlark's nest that every one passes
Because it is hidden so safe in the grasses;
A cave in the hillside for brownies to play in;

A nook in the forest for violets to stay in,
For jack-in-the-pulpits to linger and pray in;
The haunt of a wood sprite
    in yonder tree's hollow

And high on the cliffside,
the home of the swallow.

And still the road beckons, and still do I follow,
Till all wearied out, I sit down on a stile
And, oh, it is pleasant to rest there a while!
But the tireless road hurries happily on
Until at the turning it's suddenly gone.

Oh, if it were not for
my grandmother's worrying,
I'd travel right on though I'm tired of hurrying.
I'd see what's behind
every twisting and bending
Until I had followed the road to its ending!
And where does it lead, do you really suppose?
Perhaps into Fairyland; nobody knows.

But when I'm grown up
I shall find where it goes—
Shall follow and see all its wonders unfurled.
It will lead me adventuring over the world!

Making a Rainbow

Run, clouds, run;
Hide the shining sun.
Bump your curly heads together
For we want some rainy weather,
Just for fun.

Blow, wind, blow;
Make the dark clouds go.
When you have unveiled the sun
And the little storm is done,
Bend your bow.
Bend you bow of many hues,
Golds and indigos and blues;
Then walk off on quiet shoes.
Go, wind, go.

Shell Castles

A seashell is a castle
  Where a million echoes roam,
    A wee castle,
      Sea castle,
Tossed up by the foam;
  A wee creature's,
    Sea creature's
      Long deserted home.

If I were very tiny,
I should walk those winding halls
And listen to the voices
In the pink and pearly walls;
And each mysterious echo
Would tell me salty tales
Of the phosphorescent fishes
And the white-winged ship that sails
On the sea's brim
Round the earth's rim
To the lilting of the gales;
Of the sea horse
That's a wee horse

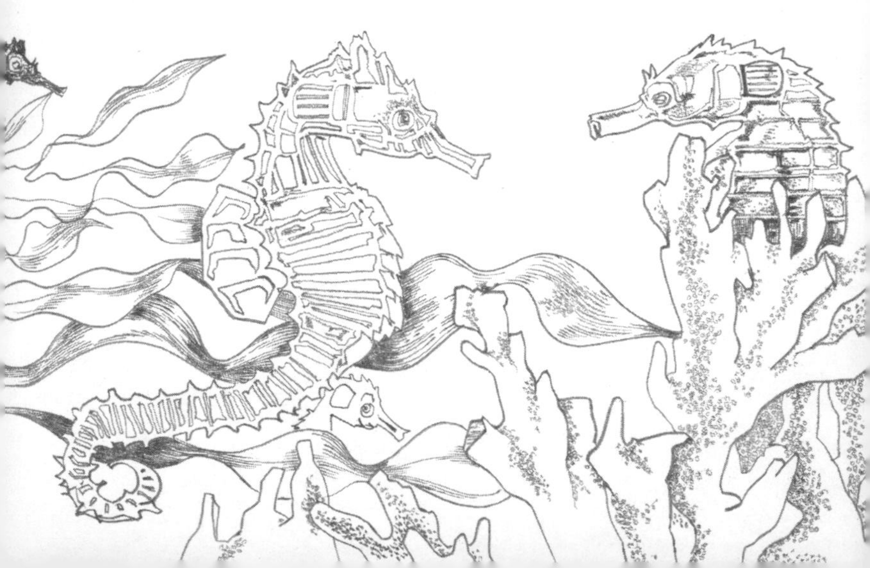

And frolics in the sea
'Neath the coral
White and sorrel
That is the mermaids' tree
And grazes on the seaweed
And the sea anemone;
But my ears cannot distinguish
The words it sings to me,
The seashell
The wee shell,
I hold so reverently,
And I only hear a whisper
Like the ghost voice of the sea.

The Crimson Balloon

The crimson balloon was
    a headstrong young thing;
He jostled his brothers and tugged at his string
And said to his master, "Let go of my tail,
And over the tops of the houses I'll sail.

I'll ride on a cloud and I'll visit the moon
(He is nothing himself but a silver balloon).
I'll bump him down into this crookedy street
And shine in his place
    with the world at my feet."

Just then came the wind
    with a cough and a sneeze
That blew him up into the pincushion trees
Where, BANG! he collapsed with a terrible sound
And wizened and shriveled,
    he sank to the ground.

Clouds

The clouds are birds that nest among the stars.
    They do not sing,
    But sleep with folded wing
Until the wind breaks through the shining bars
    Of morning, crying, "Come!"
    Then, slowly, one by one,
    They wake and fly
    Across the sky.

The Full Moon

Out of the clouds, all soapy white,
The wind blew a bubble, gleaming, bright.
It floated all night in the bowl of the sky
And burst when the first cock woke to cry.

An Autumn Play Day

Oh, Mother, may I go and play?
For all the world is playing;
The little leaves have run away,
And I can see them straying
In crimson shoes across the lawn,
Or practicing balleting.

The shadows play at hide-and-seek
Between the rows of stubble,
And every thistle stem has blown
A white and foamy bubble.

Around their holes the little moles
  All play at blind man's buffing;
The wind is turning somersaults
  With panting and with puffing.

The chipmunks play a light croquet
  And scamper through the thickets,
With partridge berries for their balls
  And bended twigs for wickets.

A dozen squirrels with tails in curls
  And feet both swift and nimble
Have found a little acorn cup
  For playing hide the thimble.

Oh, I would run and join the fun
  Without the least delaying;
Please, Mother, let me go and play,
  For all the world is playing.

Boats

The steamboat is a slowpoke,
You simply cannot rush him.
The sailboat will not move at all
Without a wind to push him.
But the speedboat, with his sharp red nose,
Is quite a different kind;
He tosses high the spray and leaves
The other boats behind.

A Fable

A willow tree once bent to look at her own
Image in a brook.
"I am the fairest tree," she cried, "In all
The wooded countryside!"

Just then a rogue wind chanced to pass
And trampled on her looking glass.
When next she looked, she was not flattered;
Her mirror and her pride were shattered.

A Brownie in a Mousetrap

I set a little mousetrap
  To catch a little mouse,
For I had heard a scuffling
Of little feet a-shuffling
  About my quiet house.
So—I set a little mousetrap
  To catch a little mouse.

But when the daylight flickered
  Across my windowsill,
And little winds came rustling
Through trees where birds were
    bustling,
  Or singing gay and shrill,
I rose to greet the morning
  And then—what should I see!
A Brownie in my mousetrap—
  Oh, goodness, gracious me!

I'd caught him by his coattails,
  I'd caught him by his shoe—
He shook his little fists at me.
  Alas, what could I do?
Too late I had discovered
  That it was not a mouse
That visited me nightly
And tiptoed, oh, so lightly
  About my quiet house.

I hurried to release him—
  He was too quick for me;
With one heroic struggle
  He wrenched his body free.
He leapt upon the windowsill
  (Now golden with the day)

And like the dandelion down
  He blew himself away.
I kept his little coattails,
  I kept his little shoe,
The one, it was a maple leaf,

The other, a carnation sheaf
(The tiniest that grew).

Since then I have not seen him
In coattails or in blouse;
But should I hear a scuffling
Of little feet a-shuffling
About my quiet house,
I would not set a mousetrap
To catch a little mouse.

Shoon

The frost wears silver slippers;
The rain wears mouse-gray shoes;
But the ragged wind goes barefoot
And wades in shining dews.

The Airplane

An airplane has gigantic wings
  But not a feather on her breast;
She only mutters when she sings
  And builds a hanger for a nest.
I love to see her stop and start;
She has a little motor heart
That beats and throbs and then is still.
She wears a fan upon her bill.

No eagle flies through sun and rain
So swiftly as an airplane.
I wish she would come swooping down
Between the steeples of the town
And lift me right off my feet
And take me high above the street,
That all the other boys might see
The little speck that would be me.

Limerick for Jim Eric

An astronaut said, "I declare!
I'll rocket right up through the air.
  I'll find out soon
  If a man's in the moon.
If not, I'll be putting one there."

Sky Harbor

There's a tower at Sky Harbor,
  And the tower wears a light
    That all the singing planes may find
      Their way to port at night.

They come like homing pigeons,
  They come from East and West,
    The light is like a mother bird
      That calls them to the nest.

Something to Think About

When airplanes get as thick as cars.
And people ride from earth to Mars,
Will traffic lights be made of stars?

A Modern Dragon

A train is a dragon that roars through the dark.
He wriggles his tail as he sends up a spark.
He pierces the night with his one yellow eye,
And all the earth trembles when he rushes by.

On Halloween

Who would ride a broomstick
  As the witches do—
    Straight across the pebbly stars
      On a street of blue?
        I should! I should!
          (If Mother came, too).

Who would take a wildcat
  With eyes all yellow-green
    To ride upon his broomstick
      Late on Halloween?
        I should! I should!
          (If Mother sat between).

Broomstick-Time

On Halloween the witches fly
  Like withered leaves across the sky,
Each with a broomstick for a steed
  That gallops at tremendous speed.
Although I don't approve of witches
  Who wear tall hats and live in ditches,
Still I am glad there is a day
  When broomsticks have a chance to play.

Dream Toys

A little dream child in a little red dress
Walks out of the sunset's loveliness
And tiptoes her way through the nursery door
And scatters her playthings all over the floor;
A ball made of silver, clean-cut from the moon,
A cricket's wee fiddle, a shadow balloon
That drifts to the ceiling; and ribbons of stars
She ties to the curtains or flings on the bars
Of somebody's bed; a fairy's lost fan,
A whistle the wind made, but dropped
as he ran,
And even a dream-horse with one hobby-hoof,
Who leaps through the window
to prance on the roof.
All of these things, and a great many more,
The dream child drops down
on the carpeted floor.
Then she calls to the girls and
she calls to the boys

Asleep in the nursery, "Come, play
with my toys.
All night I shall leave them, all night
you may play,
But when it is morning I'll take them away."

Spinning the Top

Spin, Top! Spin!
My string is white and thin;
You are red and stout;
I'll wind you all about
And toss you on your pin.
Spin, Top! Spin!

Spin, Top! Spin!
You sing when you begin,
But when you're tired out
You wabble all about.
Spin, Top! Spin!

The Butterfly and the Kite

KITE:

Oh, I am a kite
with a face and a tail!
I fly without wings
at the front of the gale;
Over the trees
and the housetops I sail,
For I am a kite
with a hood and a tail.
See that poor butterfly
down in the clover,

Beating her fragile wings
    over and over;
Hello, Butterfly,
    don't you wish you were I
Sporting about in the blue
    of the sky?

BUTTERFLY:

Hello, foolish Kite;
    why, of course it is true
That from such a height
    you've a beautiful view;
It must be delightful
    up there in the blue,
Yet I should not care
    to change places with you;
For freedom there is
    in a butterfly's wing,
But you, slavish creature,
    are tied to a string!

Come, Ride with Me to Toyland

Come, ride with me to Toyland,
  For this is Christmas Eve,
And just beyond the Dream Road
  (Where all is make-believe)
There lies a truly Toyland,
A real and wondrous Joyland,
A Little-Girl-and-Boy Land,
  Too lovely to conceive!

There Christmas fairies plant a tree
  That blossoms forth in stars

And comes to fruit in sugarplums;
There dolls and balls and painted drums
  And little trains of cars
All stand and wait for you and me
Beneath the shining wonder-tree.

So saddle up your hobbyhorse
  And ride across the night.
The thundering of our coursers' hoofs
  Will put the moon to flight;
And when the east is kitten-gray
  We'll sight that wondrous Joyland,
And at the break of Christmas Day
  We'll gallop into Toyland!

Clocks and Watches

Clocks can never hide from me,
　　Because the stupid dears
Click their little tongues so much,
　　I find them with my ears.

When Daddy says, "Please bring my watch,"
　　I tiptoe through the door
And listen at the keyhole
　　Of every bureau drawer.

I find it by the noise it makes.
　　Watches cannot play
Hide and seek as thimbles can—
　　They give themselves away.

Motor Cars

From a city window, 'way up high,
I like to watch the cars go by.
They look like burnished beetles, black,
That leave a little muddy track
Behind them as they slowly crawl.
Sometimes they do not move at all
But huddle close with hum and drone
As though they feared to be alone.
They grope their way through fog and night
With the golden feelers of their light.

Night

Night is a giant gardener
  Who does his work on high;
His black soil is the darkness,
  His garden is the sky.
The four winds are his shovel,
  The stars, his scattered seeds;
And when the clouds go blowing by
  He's digging up his weeds.
He pulls the moon up by the roots,
  And when his work is done
There blooms one great, big flower
  That people call THE SUN.

Snow

The snow is a bird, soft-feathered and white.
Silent and graceful is her flight
As she swoops to earth and spreads her wings
Over the beautiful unborn things:
Seeds and bulbs that soon will tower
Out of the nest of the ground, and flower.

Lady Sleep

Sleep walks over the hill,
A lady fair and frail.
When evening mists are chill,
When the early moon is pale,
Sleep walks over the hill.

Her hair is like a veil
And her feet are shadow-still.
The flowers close their eyes
When sleep walks over the hill.

She is beautiful and wise,
And the lonely places fill
With a hush that is deeper than sighs
When sleep walks over the hill.

Sleep walks in at the door,
And the leaping fire dies,
And the little lights go out
Like tired fireflies,

And the house dog curls on the floor
When sleep walks in at the door.

Sleep walks in at the door
    And she neither speaks nor sings,
But her breath is sweeter than song
    And folded are her wings;
And the children play no more
When sleep walks in at the door.

Title Index